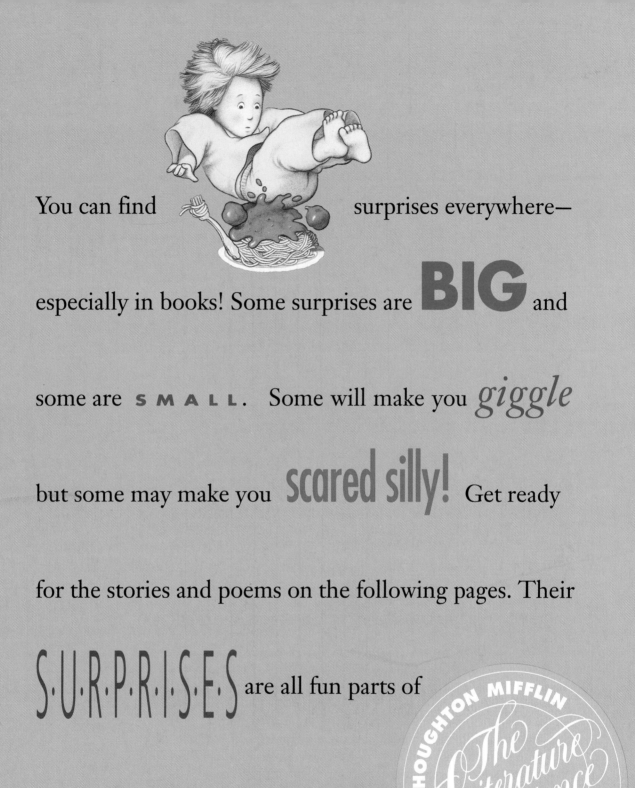

You can find surprises everywhere—especially in books! Some surprises are **BIG** and some are SMALL. Some will make you *giggle* but some may make you **scared silly!** Get ready for the stories and poems on the following pages. Their S·U·R·P·R·I·S·E·S are all fun parts of

HOUGHTON MIFFLIN The Literature Experience READING

With A Crash And A BANG!

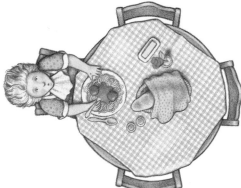

Senior Author
John J. Pikulski

Senior Coordinating Author
J. David Cooper

Senior Consulting Author
William K. Durr

Coordinating Authors
Kathryn H. Au
M. Jean Greenlaw
Marjorie Y. Lipson
Susan Page
Sheila W. Valencia
Karen K. Wixson

Authors
Rosalinda B. Barrera
Ruth P. Bunyan
Jacqueline L. Chaparro
Jacqueline C. Comas
Alan N. Crawford
Robert L. Hillerich
Timothy G. Johnson
Jana M. Mason
Pamela A. Mason
William E. Nagy
Joseph S. Renzulli
Alfredo Schifini

Senior Advisor
Richard C. Anderson

Advisors
Christopher J. Baker
Charles Peters

HOUGHTON MIFFLIN COMPANY   BOSTON
Atlanta   Dallas   Geneva, Illinois   Palo Alto   Princeton   Toronto

10

Scared Silly

BOOK 2

C A T S

Surprise!

Surprise!

You can find surprises everywhere — especially in books! These stories and poems may have some surprises for *you*!

CONTENTS

THIS IS THE
BEAR

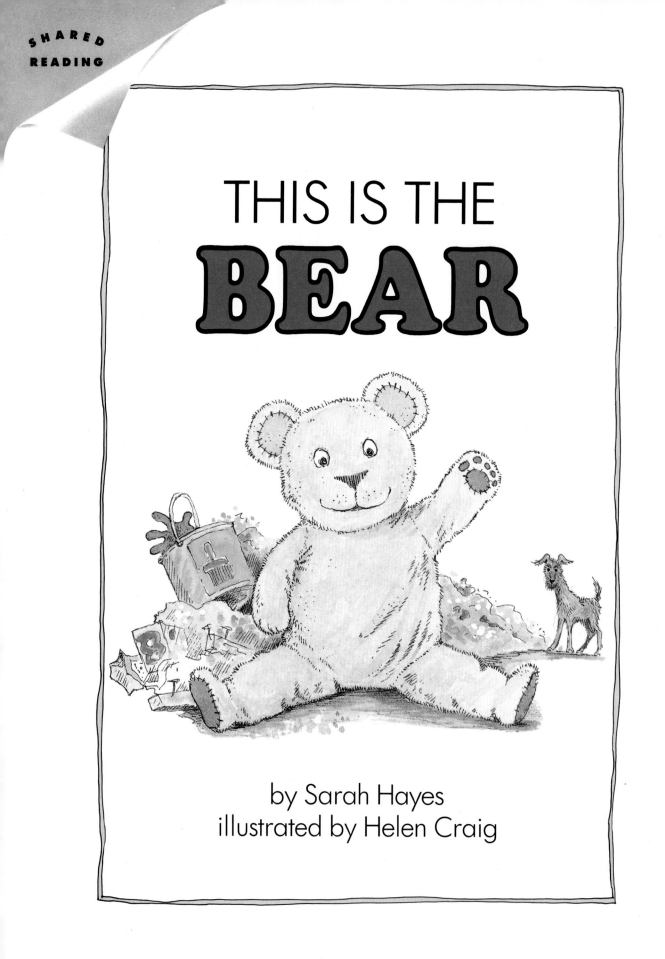

by Sarah Hayes
illustrated by Helen Craig

This is the bear
who fell in the bin.
This is the dog
who pushed him in.

15

This is the man
who picked up the sack.
This is the driver
who would not come back.

This is the bear
who went to the dump
and fell on the pile
with a bit of a bump.

Ouch!

This is the boy
who took the bus
and went to the dump
to make a fuss.

Find my bear!

You must be joking.

This is the man
in an awful grump
who searched
and searched
and searched the dump.

This is the bear
all cold and cross
who never thought
he was really lost.

Here I am.

This is the dog
who smelled the smell

of a bone

and a can

and a bear as well.

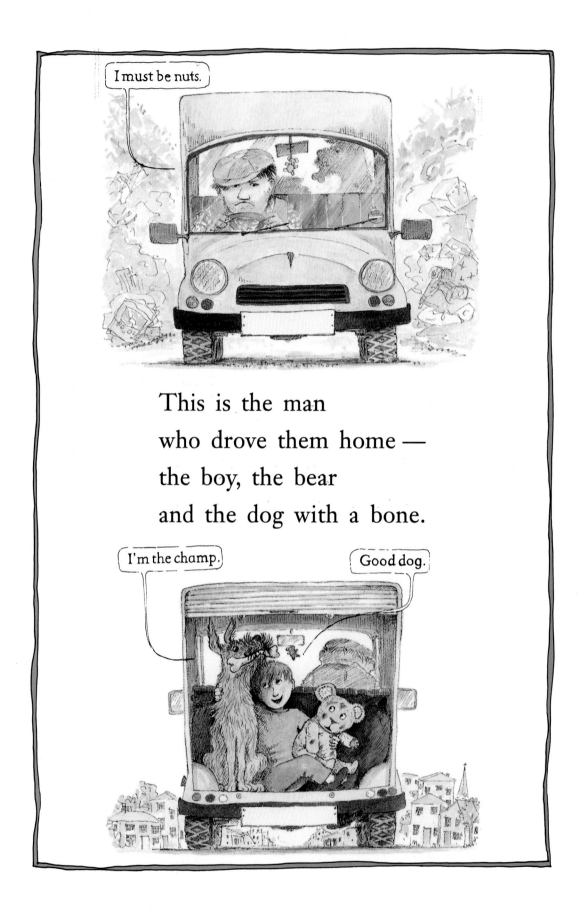

This is the man
who drove them home —
the boy, the bear
and the dog with a bone.

This is the bear
neat as a pin
who would not say
just where he had been.

A little trip.

This is the boy
who knew quite well,
but promised his friend
he would not tell.

And this is the boy
who woke up in the night
and asked the bear
if he felt all right —
and was very surprised
when the bear gave a shout,
"How soon can we have
another day out?"

Another Day Out

Did the ending surprise you? Why do
you think the bear wanted another day out?
Think of some place the boy and the
bear might go together. Draw some pictures.
Then write about your ideas.

Meet the Author

Sarah Hayes has written many books for children. Some of her other books are *Eat Up, Gemma* and *Bad Egg: The Story of Humpty Dumpty*. She also reads many children's books and then writes about them for magazines. Her reviews of these books help children and parents decide which books they want to read.

Meet the Illustrator

Helen Craig has illustrated about twenty books. She says that before making final pictures for a book, she likes to practice. She practices by making tiny pictures of all of the pages. When she knows what pictures she wants to use, she practices making the same pictures larger. Then, she carefully draws the final pictures.

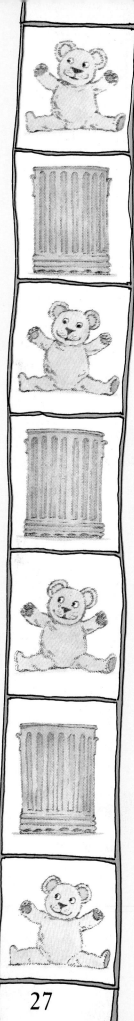

This Tooth

I jiggled it
jaggled it
jerked it.

I pushed
and pulled
and poked it.

But—

As soon as I stopped,
And left it alone,
This tooth came out
on its very own!

by Lee Bennett Hopkins

Drinking Fountain

When I climb up
To get a drink,
It doesn't work
The way you'd think.

I turn it up,
The water goes
And hits me right
Upon the nose.

I turn it down
To make it small
And don't get any
Drink at all.

by Marchette Chute

29

What is this?

AND I MEAN IT, STANLEY

by Crosby Bonsall

Listen, Stanley.

I know you are there.

I know you are

in back of the fence.

But I don't care, Stanley.

I don't want to play with you.

I don't want to talk to you.

You stay there, Stanley.

Stay in back of the fence.

I don't care.

I can play by myself, Stanley.

I don't need you, Stanley.

And I mean it, Stanley.

I am having a lot of fun.

A lot of fun!

I am making a great thing, Stanley.

A really, truly great thing.

36

And when it is done,
you will want to see it, Stanley.
Well, you can't.
I don't want you to.
And I mean it, Stanley.
I don't want you to see
what I am making.
You stay there, Stanley.
Don't you look.

Don't you look.
Don't even peek.
You hear me, Stanley?
This thing I am making
is really neat.
It is really neat, Stanley.

And it is all made now.
The very best thing I ever made.

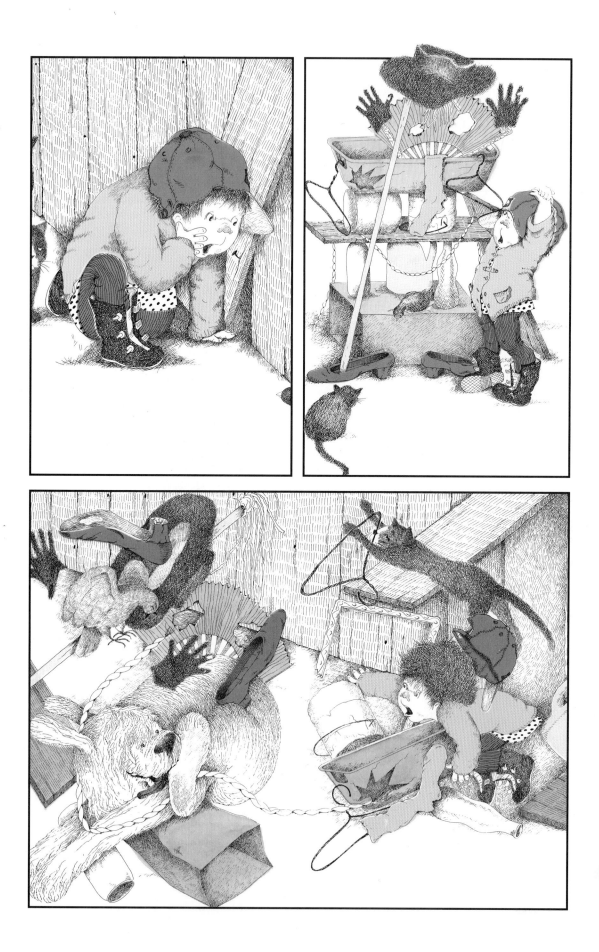

But don't you look, Stanley.
I don't want you to see it.
And I mean it . . .

STANLEY!

Aw, Stanley.

	Surprised	Not Surprised
Tommy	✓	
Sherrie		✓
Bob	✓	
Denise	✓	

Surprising Stanley

At the beginning of the story, who did you think Stanley was? Why?

Find out if your friends were surprised by the ending of this story. Make a chart to show what they thought about Stanley.

Meet the Author and Illustrator

Crosby Bonsall didn't always write and illustrate books. She once owned a business that wrote advertisements for magazines. One day she drew a small picture of this doll, named Annie Beansprout. Then she drew a whole family of dolls. Drawing these pictures gave her the idea for her first storybook. Since then, she has written and illustrated more than fifteen children's books.

What is this?

FIX-IT

by David McPhail

One morning Emma got up early
to watch television.

But the TV didn't work.

Emma asked her mother to fix it.
"Hurry, Mom!" she cried.
Emma's mother tried to fix it.
But she couldn't.

Emma's father tried.

But he couldn't fix it, either.

So he called the fix-it man. "Please
hurry," he said. "It's an emergency!"

The fix-it man came right away.
He tried to fix the TV. Emma's mother
and father tried to fix Emma.

Her father blew up a balloon . . .

until it popped.

52

Her mother sang a song.
So did the cat.

Her father pretended to be a horse —
but Emma didn't feel like riding.

Finally her mother read her a book.

"Read it again," said Emma when her mother had finished.

"And again."

"And again."

"Now *I'll* read to Millie," said Emma. And she went to her room.

Then her father found out
what was wrong with the TV.
"I fixed it!" he called.
But Emma didn't come out
of her room.

She was too busy.

Books Can Be Surprising

Did Emma like the book her mother read to her? What makes you think so? Did it surprise you that Emma liked the book more than TV?

Make a list of books you like. Then surprise a friend. Give the list to your friend, and see if he or she wants to read any of the books.

David McPhail has always liked to draw. He started to draw before he was two years old! But, by the time he was ten, he didn't want to be an artist — he wanted to be a baseball player.

David McPhail never became a baseball player. Instead he has done many other things, such as work in a factory, play in a band, make arrows, and sell greeting cards. And best of all, he now writes and illustrates books for children.

What is this?

Answers to

What is this?

Trumpet

Broccoli

Snow Geese

SURPRISES

Surprises are round
    Or long and tallish.
Surprises are square
    Or flat and smallish.

Surprises are wrapped
    With paper and bow,
And hidden in closets
    Where secrets won't show.

Surprises are often
    Good things to eat;
A get-well toy or
    A birthday treat.

Surprises come
    In such interesting sizes —
I LIKE
    SURPRISES!

by Jean Conder Soule

Surprise! Books!

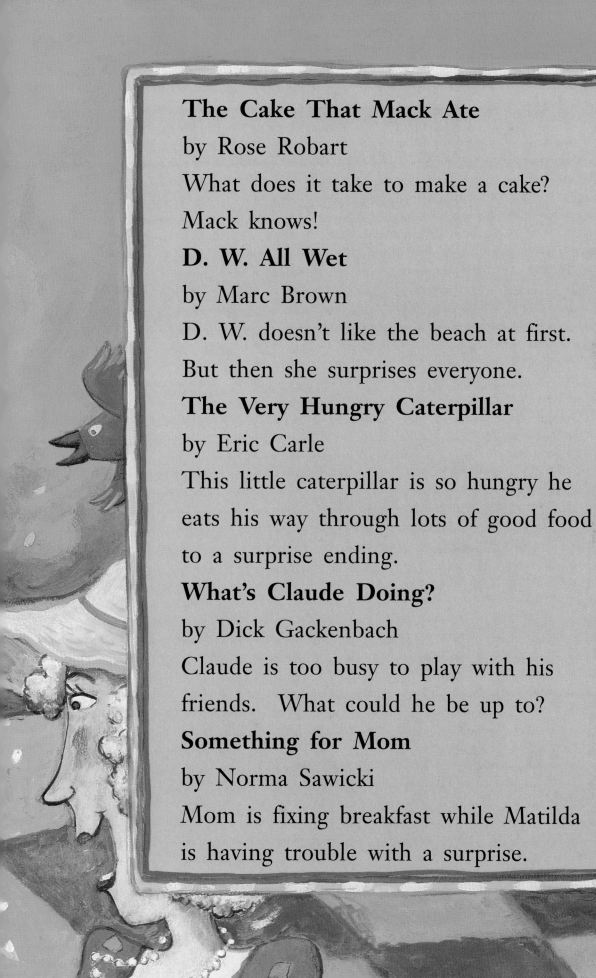

The Cake That Mack Ate

by Rose Robart

What does it take to make a cake?
Mack knows!

D. W. All Wet

by Marc Brown

D. W. doesn't like the beach at first.
But then she surprises everyone.

The Very Hungry Caterpillar

by Eric Carle

This little caterpillar is so hungry he
eats his way through lots of good food
to a surprise ending.

What's Claude Doing?

by Dick Gackenbach

Claude is too busy to play with his
friends. What could he be up to?

Something for Mom

by Norma Sawicki

Mom is fixing breakfast while Matilda
is having trouble with a surprise.

Scared Silly

Beware!!! Here are some tales that might make you feel scared silly! Get ready for some chills and thrills — and maybe some giggles, too. You never know what might be lurking on these pages!

Contents

THEY CAME TO A BRIDGE
AND RODE OVER IT,

KLIPPITY KLOP KLIPPITY KLUMP KLUMPITY KLUMPITY

THEY CAME TO A STREAM
AND RODE ACROSS IT,

KLOP KLIPPITY KLOP KERPLASH KERPLOSH KERPLASH KERPLOSH KERPLISH

THEY CAME TO A FIELD
AND RODE THROUGH IT,

THEY CAME TO A GRAVELLY HILL
AND RODE DOWN IT,

THEY CAME TO A ROCKY HILL
AND RODE UP IT,

KRINCH · KRUNCH · KRINCH · KRUNCH · KRINCH · KRUNCH · KLICK · KLACK

THEY CAME TO A CAVE
AND LOOKED IN...

KLACK . KLICK . KLACK . KLICK KLACK KLICK

A DRAGON
LOOKED OUT...

KLUMP

WELL!! THE DRAGON
DID NOT HAVE TO YELL TWICE.
DUMPLING TURNED AND RAN:

DOWN THE ROCKY HILL,
UP THE GRAVELLY HILL,

KRINCHITY.
KRUNCHITY
KRUNCHITY. KLACKITY

KLICKITY KLACKITY KLICKITY

KWISH KWISH KWISH KWISH KWISH KWISH

THROUGH THE FIELD,

KWISH KWISH KWISH KWISH KWISH KWISH KWISH KWISH KWISH KWISH
KWISH

ACROSS THE STREAM,

KROAK

KERPLASH

KERPLASH

KERPLASH KERPLASH KERPLASH KERLASH KERPLASH KERPLASH KERPLASH KLIPPITY KLIPPITY KLIPPITY KLIPPITY KLIPPITY KLIPPITY KLIP

OVER THE BRIDGE,

INTO THE CASTLE...
AND
CLOSED THE DOOR!

93

WHEW!
GOING ADVENTURING
IS A FINE THING...

KREEK KREEK
KREEK

If I Saw A Dragon . . .

What would you do if you saw a dragon?
Would you act like Prince Krispin and Dumpling?
Or would you do something else?

Tell how you would feel and what you
would do if you met a dragon. Draw
pictures, write a story, or do both.

About the Author and Illustrator

Ed Emberley wanted to draw pictures for children's books. But no one sent him stories to draw pictures for. Finally, he wrote his own book and drew pictures for it. People said that they liked it a lot.

Now Ed Emberley is a famous children's author. He and his wife, Barbara Emberley, made their barn into a workshop for writing and drawing. They work on books together in their workshop.

The Monster Stomp

by John Perry

If you want to be a monster, now's your chance
'Cause everybody's doing the monster dance.

You just stamp
your feet,

Wave your
arms around,

Stretch 'em up,
stretch 'em up,

Then put them
on the ground,

'Cause you're doing the monster stomp,
That's right, you're doing the monster stomp.
Ooh–Ah–Ooh–Ah–Ooh–Ah–Ooh–Ah!
Ooh–Ah–Ooh–Ah–Ooh–Ah–Ooh–Ah!

98

THE GUNNYWOLF

RETOLD AND ILLUSTRATED BY A. DELANEY

Once upon a time, a Little Girl and
her father lived next to a deep, dark woods.

The Little Girl never went into the woods.

Nobody did. The Gunnywolf lived there.

But one day, the Little Girl saw a flower
blooming just inside the woods.

The Little Girl forgot all about the Gunnywolf.
She stepped between the trees
and picked the flower.

And she sang,
"A B C D E F G
H I J K L M N O P
Q R S T U V
W X Y Z."

When the Little Girl looked up, she saw more
flowers. Again she forgot about the Gunnywolf.

The Little Girl skipped deeper into the
woods and picked the flowers.

And she sang,
"A B C D E F G H I J K L M N O P Q R S T U V —"

When the Little Girl looked up,
she saw even more flowers.

Again she forgot about the Gunnywolf.

The Little Girl ran deep into the woods and
picked the flowers. And she sang,

"A B C D E F G H I J K L
M N O P — "

The Little Girl was far from home.

Holding her flowers, she turned to go, and —

THERE WAS THE GUNNYWOLF!

"Little Girl!" said the Gunnywolf.

"Sing that good, sweet song to me."

"abcdefghijklmnopqrstuvwxyz,"
sang the Little Girl in a tiny voice.

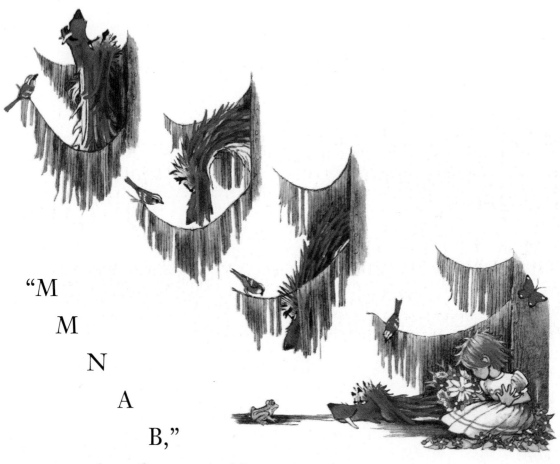

"M
 M
  N
   A
    B,"
sang the Gunnywolf,
and he fell sound asleep.

The Little Girl ran away as fast as she could.
Pit-a-pat, pit-a-pat, pit-a-pat, pit-a-pat!

The Gunnywolf woke up!

Un-ka-cha! Un-ka-cha! Un-ka-cha! Un-ka-cha!
He ran, and soon he caught up with the Little Girl.

"Little Girl!" said the Gunnywolf.
"Sing that good, sweet song again."

"A B C D E F G H I J K L M N O P Q R
S T U V W X Y Z," sang the Little Girl.

"Q
   R
      L
         S
            P," sang the Gunnywolf,
and he fell sound asleep.

Pit-a-pat, pit-a-pat, pit-a-pat, pit-a-pat!

The Little Girl ran back through the woods
as fast as she could.

The Gunnywolf woke up!
Un-ka-cha! Un-ka-cha!
Un-ka-cha!
Un-ka-cha!

He ran, and again he caught up with the Little Girl.

"Little Girl!" said the Gunnywolf.
"Sing that good, sweet song again."

"A B C D E F G H I J K L M N O P
Q R S T U V W X Y Z," sang the Little Girl.

"X
 Y
  Z
   Z
    z,"

sang the Gunnywolf, and he fell sound asleep.

Pit-a-pat, pit-a-pat, pit-a-pat, pit-a-pat!
The Little Girl ran out of the woods.

"Whew!" said the Little Girl.

But the next day and every day after that,
when the Little Girl went outside,
she gathered flowers and more flowers
and even more flowers.

And she sang,
"A B C D E F G
H I J K L M N O P
Q R S T U V
W X Y Z."

"Sing That Good, Sweet Song Again!"

The Gunnywolf liked to hear the ABC song over and over again. What other songs do you think the Gunnywolf might like?

With a friend, make a list of songs for the Gunnywolf. Share your list of songs with your class.

About the Author and Illustrator

When A. Delaney was a child she heard the story of the Gunnywolf for the first time.

The story she heard was an old tale that had been told again and again for many years. She loved hearing it so much that she told it to her own five children as they were growing up.

Finally, Ms. Delaney decided to write the story of the Gunnywolf in her own way, using her own words and her own pictures. Now you can enjoy this old tale, too!

Monsters and Dragons

Oh no! It's a monster!

Don't worry — this
monster is only a kind
of lizard. It's called
a gila monster.

112

Look out! Here comes a dragon!

This dragon doesn't breathe fire. It's a Komodo dragon. A Komodo dragon is a lizard, too.

Why do you think people call these lizards *gila monsters* and *Komodo dragons*?

A story from

OWL AT HOME

by Arnold Lobel

Strange Bumps

Owl was in bed.

"It is time

to blow out the candle

and go to sleep,"

he said with a yawn.

Then Owl saw two bumps

under the blanket

at the bottom of his bed.

"What can those strange bumps

be?" asked Owl.

Owl lifted up the blanket.

He looked down into the bed.

All he could see was darkness.

Owl tried to sleep,

but he could not.

"What if those

two strange bumps

grow bigger and bigger

while I am asleep?"

said Owl.

"That would not be pleasant."

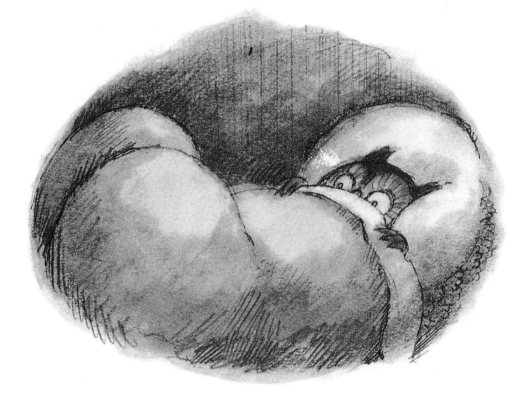

Owl moved his right foot
up and down.
The bump on the right
moved up and down.
"One of those bumps
is moving!" said Owl.
Owl moved his left foot
up and down.
The bump
on the left
moved up and down.
"The other bump is moving!"
cried Owl.

Owl pulled

all of the covers

off his bed.

The bumps were gone.

All Owl could see

at the bottom of the bed

were his own two feet.

"But now I am cold,"

said Owl.

"I will cover myself

with the blankets again."

As soon as he did,

he saw the same two bumps.

"Those bumps are back!"

shouted Owl.

"Bumps, bumps, bumps!

I will never sleep tonight!"

Owl jumped

up and down

on top of his bed.

"Where are you?

What are you?" he cried.

With a crash and a bang

the bed came falling down.

Owl ran

down the stairs.

He sat in his chair

near the fire.

"I will let those two strange bumps

sit on my bed

all by themselves,"

said Owl.

"Let them grow

as big as they wish.

I will sleep right here

where I am safe."

And that is what he did.

Hello, It's Owl

Talking with a friend about scary things sometimes makes them seem less scary.

What would you say if Owl called to tell you about the strange bumps? With a friend, act out a phone call with Owl.

About the Author and Illustrator

Arnold Lobel liked to draw so much that he drew pictures for almost 100 children's books. He liked to write funny stories about animals.

Frog, Toad, and Owl are some of the animals that Arnold Lobel wrote about. He once said that the ideas for his stories came from his own life — sometimes he felt like Frog, sometimes like Toad, and sometimes like Owl.

Lobel

A LONG-HAIRED GRIGGLE

A long-haired Griggle from the land of Grunch
Always giggled when he ate his lunch.
He'd wiggle and giggle, and munch and crunch
While nibbling the pebbles that he liked for lunch.

Alice Gilbert

More Scared Silly Stories

Monster Tracks? *by A. Delaney*
Who or what could make such big tracks in the snow? Harry bravely follows the tracks into the woods to find out.

Never Kiss an Alligator
by Colleen Stanley Bare
Some creatures in stories may scare you silly. But you're not silly to be scared of alligators!

Morton and Sidney *by Chris Demarest*
Why is Sidney, a friendly monster, out in the daytime? He belongs in Morton's closet until nighttime.

A Dark, Dark Tale *by Ruth Brown*
A black cat creeps through an old house on a dark, dark night. What is it looking for? What will it find?

BOOK 3

CATS

There are many different kinds of cats.
Some are wild, and some are tame. Some live
as pets with people. Some live in jungles or on
mountains. And some live only in our
imagination.

Here are some stories, poems, and jokes
about all kinds of cats.

CONTENTS

No One

Should Have

Six Cats!

by Susan Mathias Smith
illustrated by Steff Geissbuhler

We have six cats at my house. But soon that will change.

This morning my mom told me, "No one should have six cats, David."

I can tell that Mom thinks I should give one cat away. But which one? I love them all.

138

Herkie is cat number one. I found him in an alley one day. He had a hurt paw. He looked so sad and lonely.

Nobody knew where Herkie lived.

And nobody wanted him.

What could I do?

I had no choice.

I let him live with us.

Now Herkie's paw is all better. He can run and play and climb trees.

He and I are good friends.

I just can't give my Herkie away.

140

Zip is cat number two. She was sleeping near the bank on King Street when I found her.

Nobody knew where Zip lived.

And nobody wanted her.

What could I do?

I had no choice.

I let her live with us.

Zip doesn't do much except sleep and eat. But she's a happy cat. And whenever she's awake, she purrs.

I just can't give my Zip away.

Shadow is cat number three. I didn't find Shadow. He found me. One cold, snowy day he moved into our garage. There were some old newspapers stacked in a corner. Shadow used them as his bed.

Nobody knew where Shadow came from.

And nobody wanted him.

What else could I do?

I had no choice.

I let him live with us.

Shadow is afraid of most people. But he's not afraid of me. He lets me hold him close and pet him.

I just can't give my Shadow away.

144

Tinker is cat number four. She used to belong to my cousins. But last summer they had to move away. They couldn't take Tinker with them.

Nobody knew where Tinker would live.

And nobody wanted her.

What else could I do?

I had no choice.

I let her live with us.

Tinker sleeps under my bed. Every morning she licks my face and wakes me up.

I just can't give my Tinker away.

146

Boots is cat number five. I found him near the playground. He was just a kitten then. He was so little and afraid.

Nobody knew where Boots lived.

And nobody wanted him.

What could I do?

I had no choice.

I let him live with us.

Boots was too little to drink milk from a dish. So I fed him from a baby bottle. I saw him grow and grow. Now he is a big and beautiful cat.

I just can't give my Boots away.

148

Hairy is cat number six. Hairy once lived with Belinda, my friend at school. But Belinda's sister has a problem with cats. They make her sneeze.

So Belinda couldn't keep Hairy.

And nobody wanted him.

What could I do?

I had no choice.

I let him live with us.

At first, Hairy did not like my other cats. He would tease them and get them angry. But now Hairy and the others play and have fun together.

I just can't give my Hairy away.

What will I do?

Here comes my mom home from work now. She will say, "No one should have six cats, David. Not even us."

But I don't know which cat I want to give away.

"Mom, what do you have?" I ask. "Is that a little kitten?"

"Yes," answers Mom. "I found her outside of the office. Nobody knew where she came from. And nobody wanted her. What could I do? I had no choice. I've decided to let her live with us."

"But, Mom, you told me that no one should have six cats. Not even us," I say.

"That's right," Mom tells me. "No one should have six cats. Instead of having six cats, we should have seven!"

How About Seven Cats?

Now David and his mother have seven cats. That's a lot of cats!

Do you think you would like to have seven cats? What would be nice about it? What would be some of the problems?

Get together with a few friends to talk about having seven cats. You can make two lists — one list for the nice things and one list for the problems.

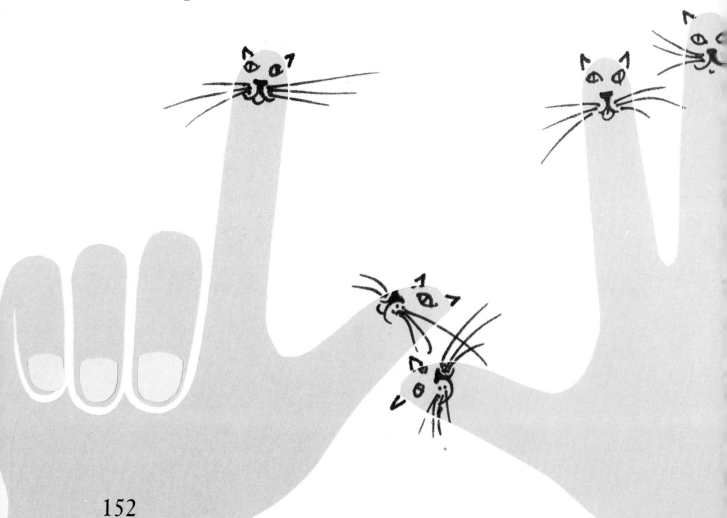

Meet the Author

Susan Mathias Smith loves animals. Maybe that is why most of the children's books she writes are about animals. She says she wants her stories to help children love and care for pets.

She says, "Sometimes when I cannot think of ideas or when I am discouraged, I go to the library and read children's books. I read until I laugh or smile . . . Then I drive home and I think and I write."

Meet the Illustrator

Steff Geissbuhler works for a graphic design company where he creates posters and signs for museums, schools, and businesses.

Favorite Poems, Favorite Cats

At Night
by Aileen Fisher

When night is dark
my cat is wise
to light the lanterns
in his eyes.

Cats
by Eleanor Farjeon

Cats sleep
Anywhere,
Any table,
Any chair,
Top of piano,
Window-ledge,
In the middle,
On the edge,
Open drawer,
Empty shoe,

Anybody's
Lap will do,
Fitted in a
Cardboard box,
In the cupboard
With your frocks —
Anywhere!
They don't care!
Cats sleep
Anywhere.

The House Cat
by Annette Wynne

The house cat sits

And smiles and sings.

He knows a lot

Of secret things.

Cat Kisses
by Bobbi Katz

Sandpaper kisses
on a cheek or a chin —
that is the way
for a day to begin!

Sandpaper kisses —
a cuddle, a purr.
I have an alarm clock
that's covered with fur.

Tiger Runs

by Derek Hall
illustrated by John Butler

Tiger is feeling so bored. Her mother
has gone hunting for food. Hunting is very
dangerous, so Tiger must stay in a safe place.

Tiger wants to play. What's that? Something is moving in the grass. She trots over to see. It's a beautiful butterfly.

Tiger tries to touch the butterfly, but it darts away. She scampers after it. Again and again she tries to catch it with her paw.

Tiger is lost! She has chased the butterfly
for such a long way. And now it is raining.
She sits down and cries like a kitten.

Suddenly, there's a noise! Tiger looks up, frightened. A huge elephant is lumbering towards her. It's the biggest animal she has ever seen.

Tiger turns and runs, faster than she has
ever run before. She is running like the wind,
and crying for her mother.

Tiger hears her mother's roar, and runs to meet her. Tiger's mother is very cross. But Tiger is so pleased to see her again.

Tiger's mother soon forgives her. They lie down, and Tiger climbs on to her. She purrs happily, feeling safe once more.

JUNGLE PLAY

What animals are in *Tiger Runs*?

How do these animals move?

What sounds do they make?

Get together with some friends to
act out the story in *Tiger Runs*.
Try to do it without using words.

Meet the Author

Derek Hall has written many books for children. His books tell about young animals and how they grow up. Here are some of the other books he has written: *Elephant Bathes, Gorilla Builds, Polar Bear Leaps, Otter Swims,* and *Panda Climbs.*

Meet the Illustrator

John Butler has always liked watching and drawing animals. When he was a boy, he would often take care of sick birds and other animals.

When he wasn't spending time with animals, he was reading books about them. He says, "I can remember studying all the illustrations and imagining the lives the animals lived."

LIONS

Lion

by N. M. Bodecker

The lion,
when he r o a r s
at night,
gives many people
quite
a fright!

The lion,
when he r o a r s
by day,
scares people near
him
far
away.

And when
he sleeps,
his lion s n o r e
is quite as scary as
his
r o a r.

TIGERS

How to Tell a Tiger
by John Ciardi

People who know tigers

      Very very well

All agree that tigers

      Are not hard to tell.

The way to tell a tiger is

      With lots of room to spare

Don't try telling them up close

      Or we may not find you there.

All Kinds

of Cats

Cats have whiskers.

Cats have paws.

Cats have soft fur.

tiger

pet

pet

lion

leopard

pet

lioness

pet

Cats run
and leap.

pet

black panther

Cats can
climb trees.

lion

pet

And all cats,
everywhere,
like to sleep
in the sun!

171

172

If I Had a Lion

by Liesel Moak Skorpen
illustrated by Steff Geissbuhler

If I had a lion, I would feed
my lion whatever he liked. If
he didn't care for vegetables,
I wouldn't make a fuss. If he
liked ice cream very much, I'd
serve it every day. My lion
would sit with us at our table,
next to me.

I'd invite my lion to share my bed. Even if it were a little crowded, my lion wouldn't mind. I could reach over in the night and know my lion was near.

We would be the best of friends.

I would wash my lion and brush his mane and even clean his teeth for him.

If he caught cold, I would put him to bed and call the doctor. If I caught cold, my lion could help my mother by carrying my tray.

A lion would be such a lot of help around the house. He could carry heavy things in his strong teeth. And when my mother made lumpy oatmeal for breakfast, my lion would help me eat it.

Everywhere I went, my lion would go. We would take long walks on summer days. And sometimes we would go to the zoo — but just for a visit.

We could carry a picnic lunch, and we would cross streets and go as far as we liked. My mother wouldn't worry because my lion would be with me.

When I got tired, I would ask my lion for a ride, and when it was time to go home, we wouldn't be lost. My lion would know the way.

We wouldn't mind staying indoors on winter days. We might just sit by the fire and talk. I would tell my lion everything I know, and he might teach me some of the things lions know.

If my mother read stories to me, my lion would listen politely, even when he didn't understand.

If ever my lion were lonely or sad, I would sit with him. I would put my arm around his neck, and I wouldn't say anything.

If ever I felt lonely or sad, my lion would sit with me. He would lay his shaggy head on my lap, and he wouldn't say anything.

But we wouldn't be lonely very often. If I had a lion . . .

If I Had a . . .

The girl in this story thought it would be nice to have a lion.

What animal would YOU like to have? What would you do together?

Draw pictures of yourself with your animal. Use the pictures to write a story. You might begin your story with the words, "If I had a . . . "

Meet the Author

Liesel Moak Skorpen gets most of her ideas for stories by thinking about her own childhood. She likes to write about what she felt and did when she was a child. She is the author of *We Were Tired of Living in a House.*

Meet the Illustrator

Steff Geissbuhler has had pet cats ever since he was a little boy. He now has a cat named "Sly."

Mr. Geissbuhler likes to draw cats and other animals. He drew the pictures in this book for *No One Should Have Six Cats* and *If I Had a Lion.* He also designed, or planned, the art for the rest of this book on cats.

CAT'S OUT OF THE BAG

by Sharon Friedman and Irene Shere

What's kitty's favorite subject in school?

Where did the cat get his new toaster?

What kind of music do cats like?

What did the cat say when he fell on his face?

What kind of cat lives under water?

What's a cat's favorite color?

 A catfish.

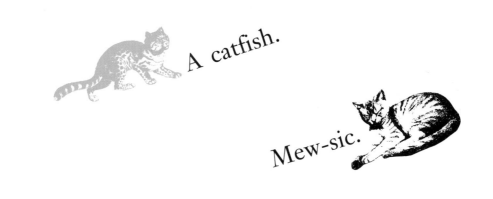 Mew-sic.

 Me-OW!

 From a cat-alog.

Purr-ple.

Cat-chy tunes.

Purr-fect Books

Charles Tiger
by Siobhan Dodds

Poor Charles Tiger
has lost his roar.
Where do you think
he will find it?

Wild Cats
by Peggy Winston

You know about lions
and tigers, but have
you ever heard of a
sandcat? Find out
more about all kinds
of wild cats.

190

The Rescue of Aunt Pansy
by Lisa Campbell Ernst

Joanne the mouse bravely rescues her Aunt Pansy from the cat. But wait — maybe it's not her aunt after all!

I Had a Cat
by Mona Rabun Reeves

This girl has a cat, a dog, and even a moose! But which does she love the best?

Kitten Up a Tree
by Keiko Kanao

Kitten gets stuck way up in a tree. Who will help her?

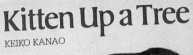

Glossary

A

angry   Jill is **angry** with Fred. She is mad because he lost her book.

B

balloon   A **balloon** is a kind of toy. You can fill a **balloon** with air to make it bigger: Lee will blow up the big, red **balloon**.

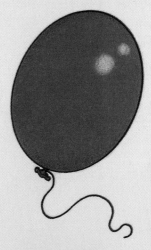

blanket   A **blanket** is a big piece of cloth. It covers you and keeps you warm: Susan got cold, so she put a **blanket** on her bed.

bump
1. If something falls with a **bump,** it makes a noise: I heard the book fall. It fell with a **bump**. 2. A **bump** is a small hill: There were two big **bumps** under my blanket. They were my two cats!

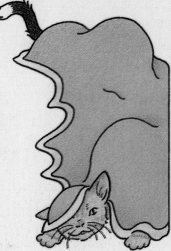

castle
A **castle** is a big building: The king and queen lived in a **castle**.

cross

1. When you are **cross,** you are angry: Andy is **cross** because the dog ran off with his ball. **2.** When you **cross** the room, you go from one side to the other: Maria and James are careful when they **cross** the street.

D

dragon

A **dragon** is a make-believe animal that is big and scary: Holly read about a **dragon** in her book.

dump

A **dump** is a place you can throw out broken or unwanted things: Joan went to the **dump** to throw out her trash.

E

emergency

The house was on fire, so the family got out right away. They called the firefighters and said, "This is an **emergency**! Come right away!"

except

Jan was the only one at home. Everyone was gone **except** Jan.

finished   Teresa read the last page of the book. After she **finished** reading it, she took a walk.

frightened   When you are scared, you are **frightened**: Carl gets **frightened** in the dark so he turns on the light.

G

great   This is a **great** book. It is the best book I have ever read!

H

hear   You **hear** with your ears: Can you **hear** the birds singing in the trees?

I

instead Roy wanted an apple, but we didn't have any. So he had an orange **instead**.

K

kitten A **kitten** is a baby cat: Luis has one big white cat and one little black **kitten**.

L

listen When you **listen**, you use your ears to hear sounds around you: **Listen!** Can you hear the train?

M

mean **1.** When I say I am cold, I **mean** it. I am not kidding. I am really cold. **2.** The brown dog is nice and friendly. The black dog will bite. He is **mean**.

neat　　**1.** Greg cleaned his room and put away all of his toys. Now his room is as **neat** as a pin. **2.** The movie was really **neat**. It was really special.

noise　　A **noise** is a sound: The loud **noise** she heard was a ringing bell.

O

oatmeal　　**Oatmeal** is a kind of cooked cereal: David likes to eat **oatmeal** for breakfast.

paw People have feet and hands. Cats and dogs have **paws:** The cat is all black with one white **paw**.

pleasant If something is **pleasant,** it is nice: Mom and I took a **pleasant** walk on the beach.

politely If you ask a question **politely,** you ask it in a nice way: "May I please have an apple?" Susan asked **politely**.

purr My cat **purrs** loudly whenever I pet her.

R

right **1.** I was sick yesterday, but now I feel all **right**. **2.** If we don't leave now, we will be late. We have to leave **right** away.

S

search If you **search** for something, you look for it: Pam **searched** and **searched** for the lost sock. Then she saw it under the bed.

shaggy Ana's dog has **shaggy** hair. When Ana brushes her dog, its hair doesn't look so **shaggy**.

sound   1. When you are **sound** asleep, it is hard to wake you up: Hugo was very tired and quickly fell **sound** asleep. 2. A **sound** is also what you hear: Do you hear that ringing **sound**?

strange   If something is **strange,** it is unusual or different. The animal in the picture is green and yellow: "What can that **strange** animal be?" asked Andy.

sweet   A nice or pleasing person, animal, or thing can be called **sweet:** Whenever I hear that **sweet** song, it makes me feel happy and peaceful.

television   You can see pictures and hear sounds on a **television:** Do you watch shows after school on **television?**

touch   Carla may **touch** the ice with her fingers. The ice will make her fingers feel cold.

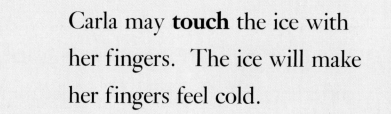

truly   If you are having a **truly** great time, you are having a really great time.

understand   Ned didn't laugh at my joke because he didn't **understand** it. I explained the joke to him and now he **understands** it.

voice   When you talk, you use your **voice**: I could hear Lisa's loud **voice** all the way upstairs.

whew   The king raced away from the dragon and into the castle. "**Whew**!" he exclaimed. "I got inside just in time!"

woods   **Woods** are places where lots of trees grow close together: Shan saw many small animals and birds on her hike through the **woods**.

Y

yell   When you **yell,** you talk very loudly: Tommy **yelled** across the playground to Kim.

Z

zoo   A **zoo** is a park where people go to see animals: You might see lions, elephants, or bears at a **zoo**.

Acknowledgments

For each of the selections listed below, grateful acknowledgment is made for permission to excerpt and/or reprint original or copyrighted material, as follows:

Major Selections

"And I Mean It, Stanley," by Crosby Bonsall. Copyright © 1974 by Crosby Bonsall. Reprinted by permission of Harper and Row, Publishers, Inc.

"Fix-It," by David McPhail. Copyright © 1984 by David McPhail. Reprinted by permission of the publisher, Dutton Children's Books, a division of Penguin Books USA, Inc.

"The Gunnywolf," by A. Delaney. Copyright © 1988 by A. Delaney. Reprinted by permission of Harper and Row, Publishers, Inc.

"If I Had a Lion," by Liesel Moak Skorpen. Text copyright © 1967 by Liesel Moak Skorpen. Reprinted by permission of Harper and Row, Publishers, Inc.

"Klippity Klop," by Ed Emberley. Copyright © 1974 by Edward R. Emberley. Reprinted by permission of Little, Brown and Company.

"No One Should Have Six Cats!" by Susan Mathias Smith. Copyright © 1982 by Susan Mathias Smith. Reprinted by permission of Modern Curriculum Press, Inc.

"Strange Bumps," from *Owl At Home* by Arnold Lobel. Copyright © 1975 by Arnold Lobel. Reprinted by permission of Harper and Row, Publishers, Inc.

"This Is the Bear," by Sarah Hayes, illustrated by Helen Craig. (J. B. Lippincott) Text copyright © 1986 by Sarah Hayes. Illustrations copyright © 1986 by Helen Craig. Reprinted by permission of Harper and Row, Publishers, Inc.

"Tiger Runs," by Derek Hall, illustrated by John Butler. Text copyright © 1984 by Derek Hall. Illustrations copyright © 1984 by John Butler. Reprinted by permission of Walker Books Limited.

Poetry

"At Night," from *Out In The Dark And Daylight* by Aileen Fisher. Text copyright © 1980 by Aileen Fisher. Reprinted by permission of Harper and Row, Publishers, Inc.

"Cat Kisses," by Bobbi Katz. Copyright © 1974 by Bobbi Katz. Used with permission of the author.

"Cats," by Eleanor Farjeon from *Eleanor Farjeon's Poems for Children*. Originally appeared in *Sing for Your Supper* by Eleanor Farjeon. Copyright © 1938 by Eleanor Farjeon, renewed 1966 by Gervase Farjeon. Reprinted by permission of Harper and Row, Publishers, Inc.

"Drinking Fountain," from *Around And About* by Marchette Chute. Copyright © 1957 by E. P. Dutton, copyright renewed 1985 by Marchette Chute. Reprinted by permission of Mary Chute Smith.

"The House Cat," from *For Days And Days* by Annette Wynne. (Lippincott) Copyright © 1919 by J. B. Lippincott Company. Copyright renewed 1947 by Annette Wynne. Reprinted by permission of Harper and Row, Publishers, Inc.

"How to Tell a Tiger," from *You Read To Me, I'll Read To You* by John Ciardi. Copyright © 1962 by John Ciardi. Reprinted by permission of Harper and Row, Publishers, Inc.

"Lion," from *Snowman Sniffles* by N. M. Bodecker. Copyright © 1982 by N. M. Bodecker (A Margaret K. McElderry Book). Reprinted by permission.

"A Long-haired Griggle," from *Poems For Sharon's Lunch Box* by Alice Gilbert. Copyright © 1972 by Alice Gilbert. Reprinted by permission.

"Surprises," by Jean Conder Soule. Copyright © 1983 by Jean Conder Soule. Reprinted by permission of the author.

"This Tooth," from *More Surprises* by Lee Bennett Hopkins. Copyright © 1970 by Lee Bennett Hopkins. Reprinted by permission of Curtis Brown, Ltd.

Others

"Cat's Out of the Bag!" by Sharon Friedman and Irene Shere. Copyright © 1986 by Lerner Publications, 241 First Avenue North, Minneapolis, MN 55401. Reprinted by permission of the publisher.

The first verse of "The Monster Stomp," by John Perry from *Game-songs With Prof. Dogg's Troupe*. Copyright © 1983. Reprinted by permission of A & C Black (Publishers) Ltd. in association with Inter-Action Imprint.

Theme Books

The Theme Books shown on pages 62, 128 and 190 are available from Houghton Mifflin Company and are reprinted with permission from various publishers. Jacket artists for these books are listed below.

The Cake That Mack Ate, by Rose Robart. Jacket art by Maryann Kovalski, copyright © 1986 by Maryann Kovalski.

Charles Tiger, By Siobhan Dodds. Jacket art by Siobhan Dodds, copyright © 1987 by Siobhan Dodds. First published in Great Britain by Orchard Books.

Monster Tracks? by A. Delaney. Jacket art by A. Delaney, copyright © 1981 by A. Delaney.

Additional Recommended Reading

Houghton Mifflin Company wishes to thank the following publishers for permission to reproduce their book covers on pages 62, 128, 129, 190 and 191.

Bradbury Press, an imprint of Macmillan Publishing Company, Inc.:
I Had a Cat, by Mona Rabun Reeves. Jacket art by Julie Downing, copyright © 1989 by Julie Downing.
Joy Street Books, an imprint of Little, Brown and Company:
D. W. All Wet, by Marc Brown. Jacket art by Marc Brown, copyright © 1988 by Marc Brown. Published simultaneously in Canada by Little, Brown and Company (Canada) Limited.
Alfred A. Knopf, a subsidiary of Random House Inc.:
Kitten Up a Tree, by Keiko Kanao. Jacket art by Keiko Kanao, copyright © 1987 by Keiko Kanao.
Macmillan Publishing Company:
Morton and Sidney, by Chris Demarest. Jacket art by Chris Demarest copyright © 1987 by Chris Demarest.
National Geographic Society:
Wild Cats, by Peggy D. Winston. Jacket photograph by Peggy D. Winston, copyright © 1981 by Peggy D. Winston.
Philomel Books, a division of the Putnam Publishing Group:
The Very Hungry Caterpillar, by Eric Carle. Jacket art by Eric Carle, copyright © 1969. Published simultaneously in Canada.
Viking Kestrel, a division of Viking Penguin Inc.:
The Rescue of Aunt Pansy, by Lisa Campbell Ernst. Jacket art by Lisa Campbell Ernst, copyright © 1987 by Lisa Campbell Ernst. Published simultaneously in Canada by Penguin Books Canada Limited, Ontario.

Credits

Program design Carbone Smolan Associates

Cover design Carbone Smolan Associates

Design 10–63 Edmund Izbickas; 64–129 Carbone Smolan Associates; 130–191 Chermayeff & Geismar Associates

Illustrations 11 David McPhail; 12–13 Roni Shepherd; 14–25 Helen Craig; 26 Valerie McKeown; 27 Helen Craig; 28 Edmund Izbickas; 31–43 Crosby Bonsall; 44 Patrick Chapin; 47–56 David McPhail; 58 David McPhail; 61 Patrick Chapin; 62–63 Roni Shepherd; 64–67 Alyssa Adams; 68–96 Ed Emberley; 97 Maxi Chambliss; 98 Rick Brown; 99–111 A. Delaney; 114–125 Arnold Lobel; 126 Diane Palmisciano; 127 Doreen Gay-Kassel; 128–129 Maxi Chambliss; 130–155 Steff Geissbuhler; 156–163 John Butler; 164–165 Steff Geissbuhler; 172–186 Steff Geissbuhler; 190–191 Steff Geissbuhler; 192 (top & bottom), 194 (top), 196, 197, 200, 202 (bottom), 204 Rosiland Solomon; 192 (middle), 193, 194 (bottom), 195, 198, 199, 202 (top), 205 Nancy Lee Walters

Photography 29 Lawrence Migdale/Photo Researchers, Inc.; 30 Steve Niedorf/The Image Bank; 44 Jeffrey Dunn; 46 Norm Thomas/Photo Researchers, Inc.; 57 Jeffry W. Myers/The Stock Market; 59 Cameron Davidson; 60 (top right) Roy Morsch/The Stock Market, (top left) David DeLossy/The Image Bank, (bottom) John Cancalos/Stock Boston; 62 Gabor Demjen/Roy Kirby, Aperture, Inc., Boston; 97 courtesy of Little, Brown and Company; 112 (top) Rod Williams/Bruce Coleman, Inc., (bottom) Jeff Foott/Bruce Coleman, Inc.; 113 (top) Norman Owen Tomalin/Bruce Coleman, Inc., (bottom) Animals Animals/© M. Austerman; 126 Adam Lobel; 167 Animals Animals/© Jim Tutek; 168 David Frazier; 169 (top) Animals Animals/© Antony Bannister, (bottom) Bernard Baudet/Superstock; 170 (top right) K. Coppieters/Superstock, (top left) Animals Animals/© LLT Rhodes, (center right) Leonard Lee Rue III/Photo Researchers, Inc., (center left) Michael P. Gadomski/Photo Researchers, Inc., (bottom right) Animals Animals/© Antony Bannister, (bottom left) Animals Animals/© Michael P. Gadomski; 171 (top right) Animals Animals/© Margot Conte, (top left) Arthus Bertrand/Photo Researchers, Inc., (center right) Anthony Mercieca/Superstock, (center left) Bradley Smith/Photo Researchers, Inc., (bottom right) Superstock, (bottom left) Stev-olaf Lindblad/Photo Researchers, Inc.

End Matter layout design by Publicom, Inc.